howliday journal

This edition published by Parragon Books Ltd in 2014

Parragon Books Ltd
Chartist House
15–17 Trim Street
Bath BA1 1HA, UK
www.parragon.com

Written by Pollygeist Danescary

ISBN 978-1-4723-5981-0

Printed in China

howliday journal

PaRRagon

Bath • New York • Cologne • Melbourne • Delhi
Hong Kong • Shenzhen • Singapore • Amsterdam

WELCOME TO YOUR HOWLIDAYS!

FUN MONSTER FREAK-OUTS AWAIT YOU!

School is out! This howliday journal has the hottest tips and tricks for having a totally clawsome howliday.

- Your friends from Monster High have travel tips. (Jetting to Scaris? Bring perfume! Going to Gloom Beach? Bring sunscream!)

- They have creeperific camping tips. (Dress to impress in your must-have pretty scary woodswear!)

- They have tips for making scareaway camp spooktacular, keeping family road trips from being a dead bore, using unbreakable code to keep in touch with your ghoulfriends and having fangtastic fun all howliday long!

Now it's time to get started, so turn the page, ghoulfriend. The howlidays are here!

Let's get amped up

for a voltage howliday! It's of spooktacular importance to keep your ghoulfriend circuits open, so you can keep in touch until school starts again. You are going to have so many new things to talk about. You'll be going to new places, meeting new people, doing new things and wearing scary-cute new clothes. So talking to your ghoulfriends will be more important than ever!

CONTACT INFO THAT YOU NEED:

Mobile numbers to add to your iCoffin contacts:

_____

_____

_____

Home numbers to reach your friends at their crypts:

_____

_____

_____

Email addresses to use for daily monster-mails:

_____@_____

_____@_____

_____@_____

Crypt addresses so you can write postcards:

_____
STREET,
_____
CITY, POSTCODE

_____
STREET,
_____
CITY, POSTCODE

_____
STREET,
_____
CITY, POSTCODE

Do you need to write a top-secret letter?
Use an unbreakable code to keep
your message secure.

Starting with any letter except **A**, write out the entire alphabet, going back to the beginning when you reach **Z**.

Now write the numbers **1** to **26** below the letters (one number under each letter).

To write a secret message, replace each letter with the number it's paired with.

Make sure your ghoulfriend knows the code, so she can decipher it!

If you start with **M**, your code will look like the one to the right. Using this chart, can you break the code below? The answer is at the bottom of the page!

8 22 23 7

___ ___ ___ ___

11 23 26 26   16 19

___ ___ ___ ___   ___ ___

17 26 15 11 7 3 1 19 !

___ ___ ___ ___ ___ ___ ___ ___ !

M	1
N	2
O	3
P	4
Q	5
R	6
S	7
T	8
U	9
V	10
W	11
X	12
Y	13
Z	14
A	15
B	16
C	17
D	18
E	19
F	20
G	21
H	22
I	23
J	24
K	25
L	26

Solution: This will be clawsome!

GHOUL GOALS

If you want to be freaky-fly when school is back in session, set some scarylicious goals for yourself!

It's important for a zombie to keep her brain in top form. And what better way to do that than to keep up with pop culture?

BOOKS TO READ:

_____

_____

_____

MOVIES TO WATCH:

_____

_____

_____

Songs to learn all the lyrics to:

_____

_____

_____

Staying in shape can be freaky fun and it's good for your fins and scales too. Keep count of how much hex-ercise you're getting! (Use a pencil so that you can easily update your total.)

Swimming: _____ laps

Skipping rope: _____ jumps

DANCING TO KILLER MUSIC: _____ songs

Write in your own favourite activity: _____
_____
_____
_____
_____

How much of your favourite activity will you do over the howlidays? _____
_____
_____
_____
_____

THIS is the perfect time to beautify the world around you. You could start a compost heap; grow your own aloe plant; start recycling paper, cans and bottles; or try a beautification idea of your own.

What beautification project will you work on?

_____

_____

Where will your **project** be? (Your house? Your garden? Your neighbourhood?)

_____

_____

Name some **GHOULFRIENDS** who can help you.

_____

_____

Get your petals in a row by setting up an action plan!

STEP ONE: GATHERING SCARY SUPPLIES

What will you need to get the most monstrous effect?

_____   _____
_____   _____
_____   _____

Which adults can help you with your project?

_____
_____
_____

STEP TWO: MAKING A DEADULE

Will you work on your beautification a few hours a week? Will you do it all at once? Make a plan here.

_____
_____
_____
_____
_____

STEP THREE: *Vine-centive*

You'll deserve a vine-tacular prize after you do all this work! What will you reward yourself with? A trip to the maul? An ice-scream cone?

_____
_____
_____

What other terrorific goals do you want to set for the **howlidays?**

GHOUL GOALS

WILD WORDS

Circle all the words that describe what your howliday will be like!

GHOUL-AMOROUS

beachy Cultured

AMPED UP

FREAKY FUN

scary-cute

VOLTAGEOUS

UGH-MAZING

BOOtiFUl

CLAWSOME

TRAVEL-FIED

golden

HOWLIDAYS STORY

FILL IN THE BLANKS in this freaktacular story about your amazing howlidays!

This **HOWLIDAY**, I am going to do some **FANGTASTIC** activities, like _____

_____, _____

and _____.

I want to wear lots of ghoul-amorous clothes,

like Draculaura's _____,

Robecca's _____

and Skelita's _____.

I'll visit my favourite shops at the **maul**,

_____

and _____.

One of the **BEAST** things about howlidays is hitting the waves. When I go swimming with the other **freshies**, I'll bring _____ _____ and _____ with me – I don't want to get sunburned! I'll listen to *howliday* songs like, "_____ _____ _" and "_____ _____", and I'll definitely go to see the BLOCKBEASTER, _____ _____.

I'm going on a trip to _____

_____. It'll be **VOLIAGEOUS!**

While I'm there, I'll probably see _____

_____ and _____,

and I hope I'll get to **EAT** _____

and _____. *Scarylicious!*

The one thing I'll have to take with me,

no matter where I go, is _____.

This *howliday* will be the best ever.

Just as Frankie always says, "_____

_____

_____

_____."

Some other things I'll do are:

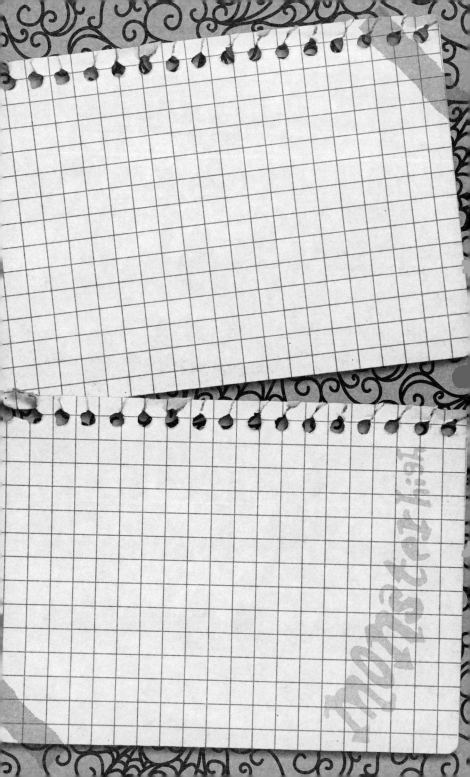

DEAD-COOL DESTINATION

HOWLiDAYS aren't complete without a ghoul-amorous trip away! You'd better dress to impress, have the most fun you can have — and be prepared for a full moon!

Where in the world are you going? Scaris, Hexico or maybe Los Ghostas? Write all about!

Will you be travelling by car, plane, boat, train or batwing?

_____

_____

_____

_____

_____

_____

_____

However you travel, you'll need to bring some **entertainment** plus extra hair gel so your fur doesn't frizz en route! What activities can you take with you?

_____

_____

_____

_____

_____

_____

Howlidays are clawsome, but some things, such as aeroplane food, are just not. What three things about your howliday are you looking forward to the least?

_____

_____

_____

_____

_____

_____

_____

What **THREE** things are you looking forward to most?

_____

_____

_____

_____

_____

_____

_____

_____

PLANEt-FRIeNDly tRAVEL....

is the best kind of travel, if you ask me. Wherever you go, you'll want to keep the oxygen fresh and the plants green.

Vine-licious Travel Tips

💀 Unplug appliances, such as the television and microwave, before you leave home. They use electricity even when they aren't on!

💀 Instead of buying lots of travel-size toiletries, fill small reusable containers with the products you'll need to stay ghoul-amorous.

💀 Bring a reusable water bottle with you. Whether you're a plant or not, you need lots of fluid!

💀 If you're staying in a hotel, ask the staff not to replace your used sheets and towels, unless you've really got your roots dirty. Reusing them saves on water!

💀 Wherever you're staying, remember to turn off the lights when you leave a room, just like at home.

💀 If you go somewhere that has brochures or maps, only take as many as you need.

💀 Don't pick any flowers or take any other wildlife out of its environment. Instead, take a picture – it'll last longer!

CHEWLIAN, my monster pet, can't always come with me when I travel. I like to bring his picture, so I don't miss him as much. It reminds me of how cute he is when he's trying to bite off someone's finger!

Which friends, pets or family members will you miss while you're travelling? Using tape or glue, attach photos or mementos of them here.

SURVIVING FAMILY TIME

ON THE ROAD, in a hotel, at the beach – you're going to be spending some time with your family. This can be a fangtastic chance to bond, but you'll also want time to yourself. How else will you daydream about all the scary-cool boys you're going to meet on howliday? You need a plan. And some of the ghouls have tips for ways you can make it out alive!

Draculaura

Deadphones are key, and I mean **KEY**. Put in your favourite tunes and drown everyone out! My favourite songs are "Blue Svede Boos" and "Greased Frightnin". What are your favourites?

_____

_____

_____

_____

_____

Operetta

Abbey

Pick up a book if you want snowbody talking to you.
My favourites are *Little House on the Glacier* and
The Wizard of Ice. What are some favourite books of yours?

_____

_____

_____

_____

_____

_____

_____

_____

_____

_____

_____

_____

_____

_____

_____

When it comes to dealing with a pack of relatives, I'm the QUEEN. The best way to keep the claws from coming out is to avoid fighting with your siblings.

- Divide all snacks evenly, or someone is gonna bare their teeth.

- No matter how tempting it is, don't invade someone else's space.

- Say *please* and *thank you* – even though they're just your brothers and sisters and you may not think they deserve it!

And you know what?

If someone in your family does something totally revolting while you're on holiday, don't keep all that anger inside. Instead, write a letter to your ghoulfriend about it. Then it'll be much easier to forgive and forget.

Write your letters on the next few pages:

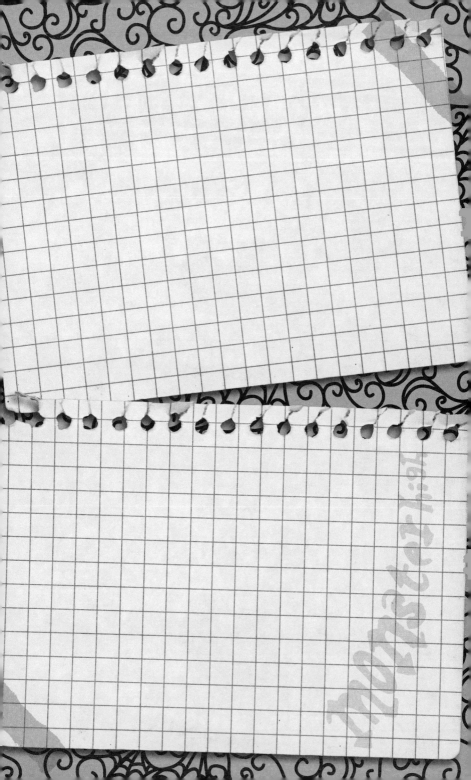

EVERYSCARE YOU GO

ACCORDING to

paragraph 8.12 of the Gargoyle Code of Ethics, it is a gargoyle's responsibility to ensure that travellers are prepared for their journeys. Make a list of travel essentials that you will need no matter where you go, and then check that list several times to make sure you haven't missed anything.

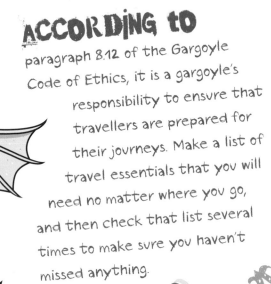

Ghoulia

TOILETRIES

From skin scare to dental hygiene, clean claws to tidy fur, taking care of your body should be a top priority! Start with this list and add your own items.

- toothpaste
- toothbrush
- dental floss
- facial cleanser
- body wash
- shampoo
- conditioner
- nail file
- hairbrush

Socks and Underscare

Very important! Bring one clean pair for every day you'll be on holiday, plus three extras.

MONSTERTAINMENT

It is **IMPORTANT** that you bring some solid monstertainment, or you may become bored. Bring some of the items on this list and add your own.

- MP3 player
- iCoffin
- books and magazines
- board games

- snacks
- paper
- pens, pencils or crayons

- _____
- _____
- _____
- _____
- _____
- _____
- _____
- _____
- _____
- _____

- _____
- _____
- _____
- _____
- _____
- _____
- _____
- _____
- _____

SET YOUR PLANS IN STONE

As a gargoyle, it is my job to warn you about the importance of planning ahead. No matter where you go on howliday, you should think carefully about what you will pack, what you will do while you are there and all the different ways you can have some rock-solid fun. If you are prepared, you will have a *très* good time.

On the following pages you will find suggestions to help you pack – I cannot emphasize enough how important **sunscream** is.

You'll also find ideas for ghoul-amorous fashion, scarylicious snacks and super-solid games and activities – all perfect for travelling.

ROCHELLE

ROAD RAGING

Road trips can be very exciting. *Par exemple,* you can drive through new cities, listen to rock music and read lots of amusing signs. But remember to follow these rules of the road:

- 💀 Let the driver concentrate. If there's bad weather or a lot of traffic, you may need to be quiet or you could end up in a rocky situation.

- 💀 Keep your snacks and games where you can easily reach them.

- 💀 And, of course, use the ghouls' room every time you make a stop!

A road trip with your family offers opportunities for reading, eating ghoulicious fast food and more reading. But you can liven up the ride if you bring the right supplies....

Packing List:

- travel pillow and blanket
- easy-to-access backpack
- travel games
- deadphones and MP3 player
- sketchbook and coloured pencils
- cereal bars, crisps and fruit
- stylish slip-on shoes
- fangtastic light-weight goes-with-everything jumper to wear

_____

_____

_____

_____

_____

_____

_____

_____

_____

_____

GHOULIA'S GAMES

Keep your brain busy with some terrorific games.
They will help make the time fly!

SKULLS AND CROSSES

Play against a friend or sibling – who will be the first
to get three in a row?

ZOMBIE-RIFIC WORDSEARCH

To rev up the language centre of your brain, find all the *Monster High* words on this list. Look up, down, across, diagonally and backwards!

CAPITAL
CASKETBALL
CLAWD
CLAWSOME
DEUCE
FEARLEADING
FLASHION

GOREGEOUS
GIL
GOLDEN
HEXICO
HOLT
iCOFFIN
JACKSON

MOE
MONSTERS
SCARIS
SPHINX
VOLTAGE

Check your answers at the back of the book.

SNACK ATTACK

To keep your fin up while you're on the road, pack some nibbles! Try this fishy cracker recipe!

Goldfish Crackers

You'll need:

- ★ 225g grated Cheddar cheese
- ★ 225g flour
- ★ 60g butter, cut into cubes
- ★ 3/4 teaspoon salt
- ★ 2 tablespoons hot water

Instructions:

1. With the help of an adult, preheat the oven to 180°C.

2. Place the cheese, butter, flour and salt into a food processor and blend until the mixture looks like coarse sand.

3. Add the hot water to the food processor, one tablespoon at a time. Keep mixing until the ingredients combine into a dough.

4. Remove the dough from the processor and form into a small, tidy ball. Wrap in cling film and leave to chill in the fridge for 20 minutes.

5. Once chilled, roll out the dough thinly (5mm).

6. With the help of an adult, cut lots of little fish shapes into the dough. You could use a cookie cutter or a blunt knife.

7. Place the fish shapes on a lined baking tray and bake at 180°C for about 15 minutes.

Lagoona

GHOUL-AMOUR ON THE GO

BARE-BONES TRAVEL STYLE

When you're on the road, you have to make a little fashion go a long way! Bring along these **bonita** accessories to brighten your travel look.

- **LIGHTWEIGHT SHAWL OR SUMMER SCARF** — Wrap around your shoulders when it's chilly in the car and turn it into a belt when you stop at the services!

- **OVERSIZED SHADES** — Guard your sockets from the sun by wearing chic oversized shades. Indoors, they double as a headband! Plastic is best; metal will get caught in your hair, and *dios mío*, that can hurt!

- **BLACK SHORTS** — The ultimate in versatility. These can be casual for a day in the park, but add a cute top and they are ghoul-amorous for a dinner.

Skelita

SPLIT POLTERNALITY

Game time in the car will help you avoid being dead bored. Try making up your own monster personalities!

One at a time, players make the **GHOULIEST** face they can — and make up a funny name and voice to go with it. Using your new face and voice, tell a story about your new persona! Talk about who your new character is — Sea monster? Werewolf? — and about a time when your character was in danger, won something or learned something new. How does it end? Everyone will be dying to find out!

ghouls RULE

Ready for another fangtastic game for the whole family? Try planning this ghoulish picnic together!

ALPHAFRIGHT PICNIC

The goal of Alphafright Picnic is to make a list from A to Z of all the things you're going to bring to a picnic. In alphabetical order, each player adds an item to the list. Every player has to list each item that is being brought.

HERE'S AN HEXAMPLE:

- **Ghoul One:** "I'm going on a picnic and I'm bringing an alligator."
- **Ghoul Two:** "I'm going on a picnic and I'm bringing an alligator and a bat."
- **Ghoul Three:** "I'm going on a picnic and I'm bringing an alligator, a bat and a coffin."
- **Ghoul Four ...** has to come up with a word that starts with the letter D. Then, name all the items, including the new one.

A few more rules of the game:

- Once everyone has added a word, it's Ghoul One's turn again.
- Keep playing in the same order all the way through to the end of the alphabet.
- If you can't come up with a word for your letter, or you forget any of the items on the list, you're out of the game. The winner is the last ghoul standing!

CREEPERIFIC CAMPING

Nature is naturally gore-geous, so if you get to go camping, you're scary lucky. There will be all kinds of things to do, such as hiking and toasting marshmonsters. And, of course, taking care of the plant and animal life around you!

CREEPERIFIC CAMPING PLANNING

What three plant-tastic camping activities will you do?

1. _____

2. _____

3. _____

CREEPERIFIC CAMPING

Spending time in the countryside will help you get in touch with the environment. You'll need to pack things you can do outside. And make sure your iCoffin is fully charged before you leave!

Packing List:

- tent
- sleeping bag and pillow
- torch and batteries
- solar charger for your iCoffin
- insect spray
- whistle
- hand sanitizer

- sketchbook and coloured pencils for drawing pretty scary sightings
- nuts, dried fruit and cereal bars
- water in reusable bottles
- scary-cute hiking boots

_____ _____
_____ _____
_____ _____
_____ _____
_____ _____
_____ _____
_____ _____
_____ _____

GHOUL-AMOUR ON THE GO

Fabulous Fur, Claw Care and MONSTER STYLE

Whatever you do, don't forget to take care of your fur, or *it* will take care of you! When you're in the woods, you can try a couple of different things.

TAILSIDE

1. Gather your hair on one side of your head, a little below your ear.

2. Leave out a strand of hair from underneath.

3. Secure your hair with a hairband. Don't be afraid to let it look a little messy!

4. Now that you've formed the tail, wrap the loose strand around the elastic to cover it.

5. Tuck the end of the loose strand into the tail.

Freaky chic!

SINGLE SNAKE

1. Pull your hair into a low ponytail at the back of your head, leaving some hair loose around your face.

2. Tease the hair in the ponytail by running a comb back and forth along the hair.

3. Keeping the hair in the front separate, remove the hairband from the ponytail.

4. Separate the hair from the ponytail into three sections and plait them together very loosely.

TOO GHOUL
FOR SCHOOL!

WILD CLAWS

CLAW CARE is important too, so blend in with the wildlife with some leopard print claws. You'll need a clear top coat, beige and blue nail polish and a black nail-art pen.

1. Paint your nails beige.

2. When the beige layer is completely dry, dot on some blue blobs – four to seven per nail. They don't need to be even or symmetrical!

3. Wait for the blue layer to dry completely too. Then, very carefully, partially outline each blue blob with black.

4. Once your nails have finished drying, add the shiny top coat.

NOW YOU'RE A REAL WILD CHILD!

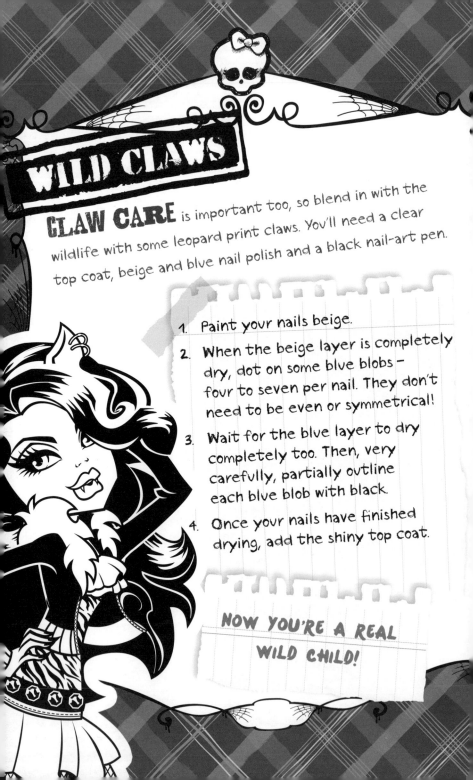

MONSTER STYLE

Fashionista that you are, you know you need to look *scary-cute* while you're camping. Jean shorts, vest tops and chic hiking boots are the way to go. Draw your most ghoul-amorous camping outfit on the next two pages! Of course, your fierce fashion will need to be a perfect monster match for hiking, dealing with nature's creepy-crawlies and getting your claws dirty.

BE YOURSELF
BE UNIQUE
BE A MONSTER

SNACK ATTACK

It is **very important** to keep your energy up while you're inhaling all that fresh oxygen, and the best way to do that is with healthy snacks. This recipe was passed down from troll to troll, so it's a guaranteed scarylicious feast.

Troll Mix

You'll need:

- ⭐ 125g unsalted cashews
- ⭐ 125g unsalted almonds
- ⭐ 125g dried cranberries
- ⭐ 125g dried cherries
- ⭐ 150g semi-sweet chocolate chips

Instructions:

1. Pour all the ingredients into a medium-sized bowl.
2. Stir together with a large spoon.
3. Store in an airtight container.
4. To snack on the go, transfer a few handfuls to a sandwich bag.

FRIGHT
ON

INSPECTRA YOUR SURROUNDINGS

It is your duty to report on your findings in the woods, so make sure to take the time for a freakishly fabulous scavenger photo hunt.

Circle each of the items that you are able to find below. If possible, take pictures so you'll have photographic evidence.

ACORN
bird
INSECT
butterfly
GHOST TRACKS
ghouls' room sign
HAUNTED TREE

log cabin
MISTY MOUNTAINTOP
purple ferret
SPOOKY STREAM
squirrel
TROLL-FACED BOULDER
wildflower

Add your own freakishly fabulous finds:

_____   _____

_____   _____

_____   _____

_____

The main reason for a **VAMPFIRE** is to tell spooky stories! Tell your own spooky story and don't forget to include some of the spooky story moments below!

"... but her head was only attached to her neck by the stitches!"

"... and then the bootiful girl ran off into the woods alone!"

"... but the tapping wasn't coming from her ghoulfriend's claws. It was coming from the roof!"

"... and the call was coming from an iCoffin ... inside her house!"

NOW WRITE YOUR STORY....

SPOOKY STORY MOMENTS

It was a dark and stormy night, and ...

My holidays are
amazing Paris

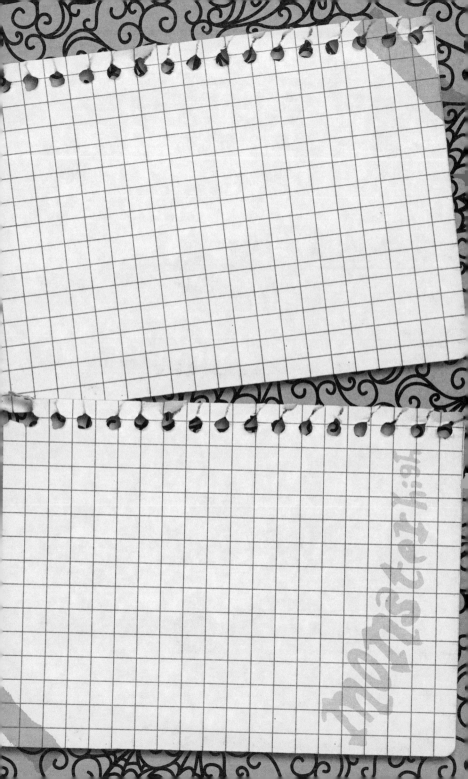

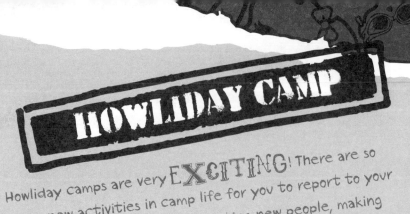

HOWLIDAY CAMP

Howliday camps are very EXCITING! There are so many new activities in camp life for you to report to your family and friends. You'll be meeting new people, making crafts, playing sports and having all kinds of spooky fun. Be sure to take lots of pictures and keep notes on what you're doing so you can gossip about it later.

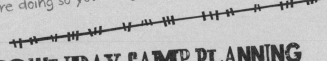

HOWLIDAY CAMP PLANNING

What three activities are you looking forward to most?

1. _____
_____
_____

2. _____
_____
_____

3. _____
_____

At camp, you'll be the new girl – but so will everyone else! Voltage! All you need to do is bring the right stuff. You'll be sleeping away from home for a week or more, so pack enough to last for the whole time. And bring some killer outfits, of course. Add your items to the list!

PACKING LIST:

- freaky chic sheets, blanket and pillow
- stylish sleepwear – hel-*lo*, eye mask!
- pictures of your family and friends
- scarylicious snacks to share
- books, magazines and music
- stationery, pens, addresses and stamps

_____
_____
_____
_____
_____
_____
_____
_____
_____
_____
_____
_____

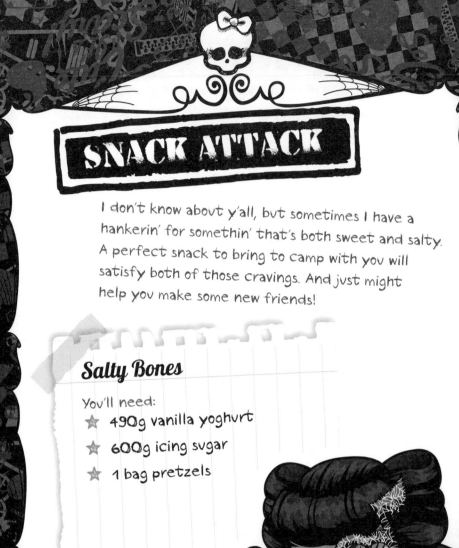

SNACK ATTACK

I don't know about y'all, but sometimes I have a hankerin' for somethin' that's both sweet and salty. A perfect snack to bring to camp with you will satisfy both of those cravings. And just might help you make some new friends!

Salty Bones

You'll need:
- ⭐ 490g vanilla yoghurt
- ⭐ 600g icing sugar
- ⭐ 1 bag pretzels

Operetta

Instructions:

1. With an adult's help, preheat the oven to 120°C.
2. Place the yoghurt in a large mixing bowl. Add the icing sugar, a little at a time, and combine with a hand blender until it's completely mixed into a thick icing.
3. Using tongs or chopsticks, dip the pretzels into the icing one at a time, then place them on a wire cooling rack.

Tip: Place a baking tray under the rack to catch any drips.

4. Once all the pretzels are coated, turn the oven OFF and place the wire rack and baking tray on the middle shelf, leaving the oven door slightly open.
5. Allow the icing to harden for 3 to 4 hours.
6. After they've cooled, they're ready to eat! You can store your salty bones in an airtight container for up to three days.

Safety first, ghouls!

According to paragraph 18.6 of the Gargoyle Code of Ethics, it is of the utmost importance to listen to your camp leaders so that you stay safe. Be on time for camp activities, keep your room or tent clean ... and have a rocking good time!

GET FIRED UP!

GUIDE TO GETTING INSPIRED....

Whether you are making a bracelet or a sculpture or writing a play or a letter, there are many ways to light your creative fire. Try letting your thoughts take flight with some of these tricks!

Story ideas:
Make your mind a blank sheet of paper and see what pops into it. Write the ideas here:

_____

_____

_____

_____

_____

_____

_____

_____

_____

_____

_____

_____

_____

_____

_____

_____

ART IDEAS: Look at magazines for colours, shapes and patterns. What do they make you think of? Cut out the images that inspire you (make sure you have permission first!) and glue them here.

Fashion ideas: Search for new possibilities in the world around you. Go to the garden, the kitchen or the maul. What fashion inspiration did you find?

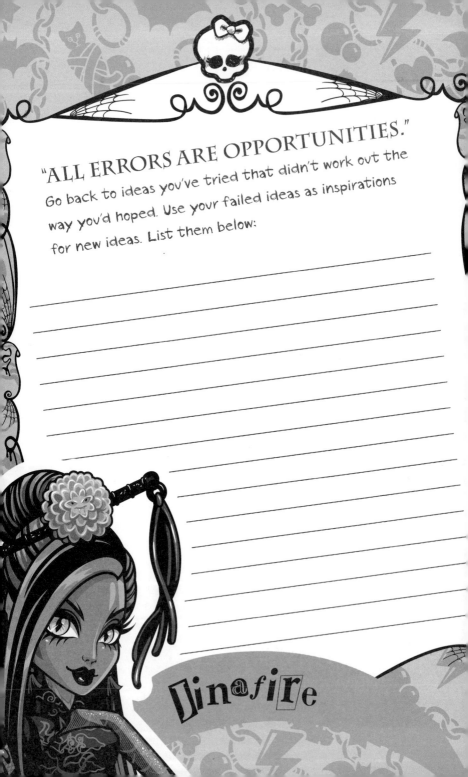

"ALL ERRORS ARE OPPORTUNITIES."

Go back to ideas you've tried that didn't work out the way you'd hoped. Use your failed ideas as inspirations for new ideas. List them below:

Jinafire

GHOUL-AMOUR ON THE GO

Nails in Stitches

Amp up your nail routine with some high-voltage stitches! You'll need a clear top coat, a black nail-art pen and nail polish that isn't too dark. Mint green is super sparky, but white or pink are good choices too!

1. Paint your nails with your colourful polish.

2. After the polish has dried, use the black nail-art pen to draw a diagonal line on the nails of your ring fingers and thumbs (or all your nails if you like!) Make sure the lines are different lengths and not symmetrical.

3. Now use the pen to draw two or three evenly spaced stitches across each diagonal line.

4. Once your nails are completely dry, add the shiny top coat.

SO ELECTRIC!

TOUGH AS SCALES

One of the beast things about camp is all the bat-letic activities that are available. Casketball, fearleading, swimming ... they all make my gills flutter with excitement! If you want to be at your best, you need to give your fins a good workout. Here are some hexercises to keep you in seafaring shape!

OCTO-STRETCH

1. Stand straight with your arms stretched over your head. Reach as high as you can for eight slow counts.

2. Slowly curl your spine down until you're touching your toes. Reach as low as you can for eight slow counts.

3. Slowly curl your spine back up. Spread your legs to the width of your shoulders.

4. Lift your arms over your head, stretch them up, and then bend from the waist to your right, still facing ahead. Reach as far to the right as you can for eight slow counts.

5. Slowly bend back up to the centre, with your arms still lifted over your head.

6. With your arms still stretched up, bend from the waist to your left, still facing ahead. Reach as far to the left as you can for eight slow counts.

7. Slowly bend back up to the centre.

8. Gently shake your arms and legs.

CLAM CRUNCHES

1. Lie on your back.
2. Bend your knees, bringing your feet towards your bottom, then lift your feet up off the floor and cross your legs at the ankles. Your feet should be dangling above the floor.
3. Using your stomach muscles, pull your upper body towards your knees and exhale.
4. Release your upper body, inhaling as you lie back down, knees still bent.
5. Repeat ten times, then have a break.
6. Do three more sets of ten, taking a break between each set.

SEAL JUMPS

A seal jump is almost the same as a star jump, but instead of raising your hands over your head, clap them in front of you – like a seal. How many can you do in a row?

KEEPING A JOURNAL

Sometimes new places, PEOPLE and routines can get a ghoul all steamed up. Keep your rivets in place and your metal oiled by writing regularly to yourself about all the robotastic activities you're doing at camp, not to mention the friends you're meeting and the outfits you're wearing. Time can slip away faster than a cog rolling downhill, so don't forget to write!

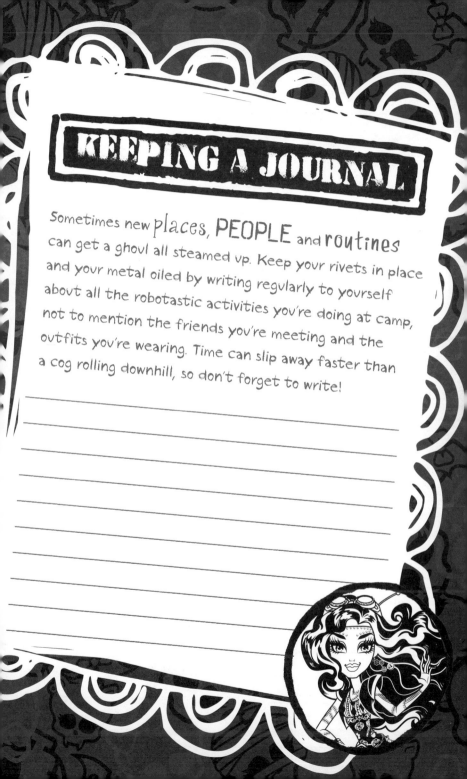

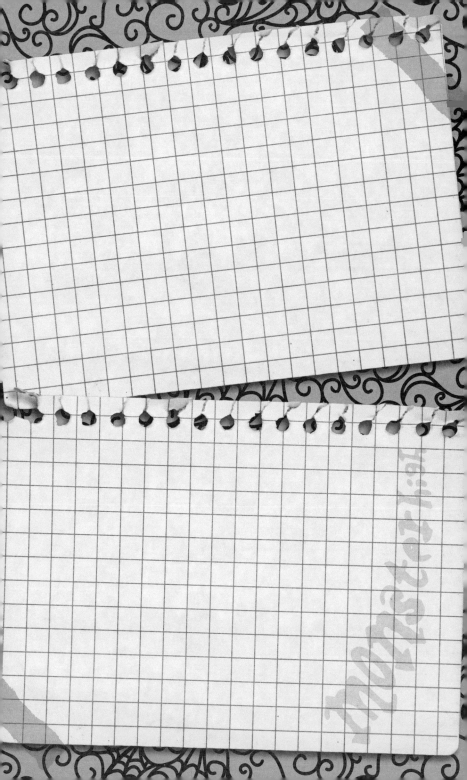

GLOOM BEACH

Going to **GLOOM BEACH** is the best way to spend the howlidays, gillfriend. The sun will be sizzling hot and reflections from the water and the sand will make it even hotter, so take care of those scales by applying sunscream regularly. And some advice from Down Unda: *Stay hydrated!*

Gloom Beach Planning

What are three frightfully fabulous things you want to do at the beach?

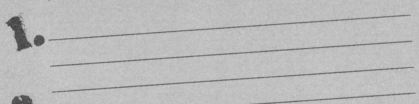

1. _____
_____

2. _____
_____

3. _____
_____

LAgooNa

If you're going to the beach, mate, you'll need to be ready for a fintastic time! Pack your screechbag with all the sandy basics, and remember to bring lots of water – if you're a freshie, you can't drink the seawater!

PACKING LIST:

- 💀 swimsuit
- 💀 scary-cute wide-brimmed hat
- 💀 freaky fly shades
- 💀 sunscream
- 💀 towel
- 💀 terrorific beach read or magazine
- 💀 Frisbee™
- 💀 bucket and spade
- 💀 cool box with fresh fruit and water

- 💀 _____
- 💀 _____
- 💀 _____
- 💀 _____
- 💀 _____
- 💀 _____
- 💀 _____
- 💀 _____
- 💀 _____
- 💀 _____
- 💀 _____
- 💀 _____

Keeping **COLD** is best way to enjoy heat. Important to ice up, so you do not lose your cool.

Tips on Keeping Cold

- 💀 Bring cool box full of ice. Stick face inside if necessary.

- 💀 Wear wide-brimmed hat. Stylish like a fox. Keeps sun off face.

- 💀 Rent beach umbrella. Shape is similar to igloo. Makes you cool. When you need break from sun, hang like bat under umbrella.

- 💀 Eat ice scream, ice lolly, fresh fruit. All are cool and sweet.

SO Cool

BEAST BOOKS

You should always bring something to read with you, and an old favourite is just as good as something new. My favourite books are *Pride and Poltergeist*, *A Zombie Grows in Beastlyn* and *Maniac Monstergee* – and of course I like to read *Dead Fast* comic books. What are your favourite books and comics?

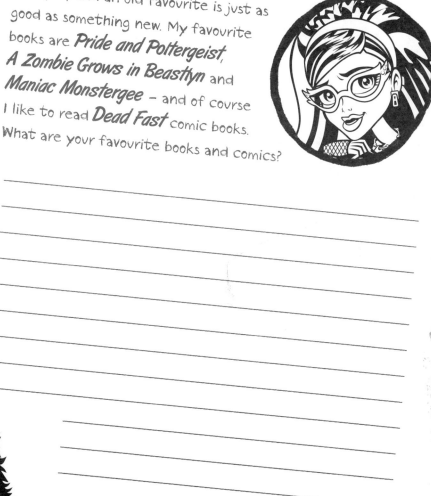

SNACK ATTACK

You need to keep your **energy** up when you're at Gloom Beach because there is so much to do. Try this scarylicious snack when you need a boost. It is healthy, and the fruit colours are fangtastic and romantic.

Fruit of the Gloom

You'll need:
- ⭐ 150g grapes
- ⭐ 150g pineapple, cubed*
- ⭐ 150g watermelon, cubed*
- ⭐ Cocktail sticks

F G

Instructions:

1. Slide one watermelon cube, one grape and one pineapple cube on to each cocktail stick.
2. Carefully pack the skewers of fruit into a flat container.
3. Keep them in a cool box with ice blocks until you're ready to eat them.

*TIP: If the pineapple and watermelon aren't already cubed, cut them into 3 cm cubes with help from an adult.

LAGOONA BLUE'S TEST OF FALSE OR TRUE

The more you know about the beach, the more fin you can have while you're here. Get a scaleful of these statements and circle 'false' or 'true' for each one. Then turn the page upside-down to check your answers!

1. My father is the Sea Monster. **FALSE** **TRUE**

2. The ocean covers 71 per cent of Earth's surface. Salty heaven! **FALSE** **TRUE**

3. Pearls get that ghostly shimmer from being made by a grain of sand inside an oyster's shell. **FALSE** **TRUE**

4. Fearleading Camp takes place at North Gloom Beach. **FALSE** **TRUE**

5. The ocean contains nearly 20 million tons of gold. So ghoul-amorous ! **FALSE** **TRUE**

6. The average depth of the ocean is about 80 metres – much deeper than the Monster High catacombs. **FALSE** **TRUE**

1. True! And my mother is a water nymph.
2. True! It makes up 97 per cent of Earth's water.
3. True! That's why they look so fintastic with my skin tone.
4. False! Fearleading Camp takes place at South Gloom Beach.
5. True! But most of the gold is dissolved into pieces so tiny that you can't see them. (Don't tell Cleo, she'll be disappointed!)
6. False! The average depth of the ocean is about 4km – much, much deeper than the Monster High catacombs!

GHOULAMOUR ON THE GO

Skin Scare Safety Tips for Sunny Days

Skin scare is incredibly important. Your skin covers your whole body and you want it to be healthy and soft, so you have to take extra precautions when you go to Gloom Beach.

SKIN SCARE TIPS

💀 Midday sun is the hottest, so be extra vigilant between 11 am and 3 pm.

💀 Apply sunscream to dry skin and allow 30 minutes for it to soak in before you go out into the sun.

💀 Reapply your sunscream every 90 minutes. You can still get a totally golden tan, even with sunscream on.

💀 Remember your lips! Use a lip balm with an SPF.

💀 Salt water dries out most monsters' skin, so rinse off in the beach shower when you leave the water. You want to **visit** the desert; you don't want your skin to **be** the desert.

💀 When you're done for the day, apply a moisturizer all over to keep your skin royally smooth!

GHOUL-AMOUR ON THE GO

Looking like a Sphinx in the Sand

Just because you're at the beach, there is no reason to look less than absolutely golden. Every hair must be in place if you want to be a Beach Queen.

Cleo De Nile

Beach beasties have to be fashionable, of course. You'll need to bring the perfect swimsuit — or better yet, two. You'll need stylish sandals and don't forget a monsterific summery skirt and top to wear on the way there and back. And *only* wear oversized accessories for the beach, ghouls. Anything too small might get lost in the sand.

Perfectly IMPERFECT

ROYAL LIPS

Not just **any**one can have perfectly glossed lips. To get yours, use a shimmery lip gloss in a peach or pink shade. Try to find one with both SPF (for sun protection) and moisturizer.

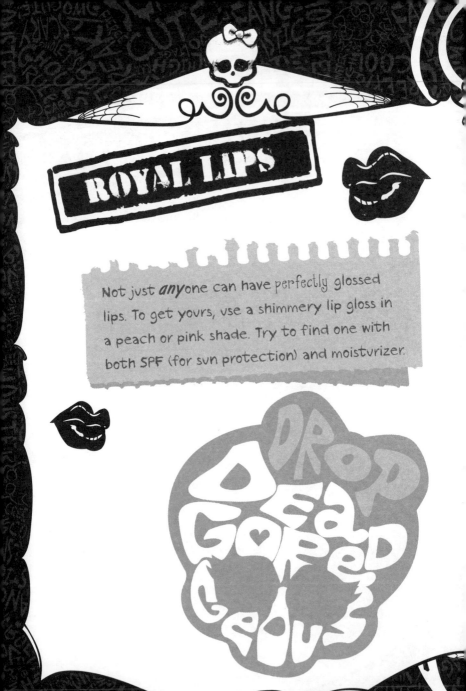

DROP DEAD GORGEOUS

DYNASTIC 'DO

1. Sneak some tiny, snakelike plaits into your hair. Sssssuper chic.

2. Select one or two sections of 2 or 3 cm on each side of your head.

3. Plait them, and secure with very small hairbands.

4. When you're not in the water, add a wide headband to the look if you really want to be regal.

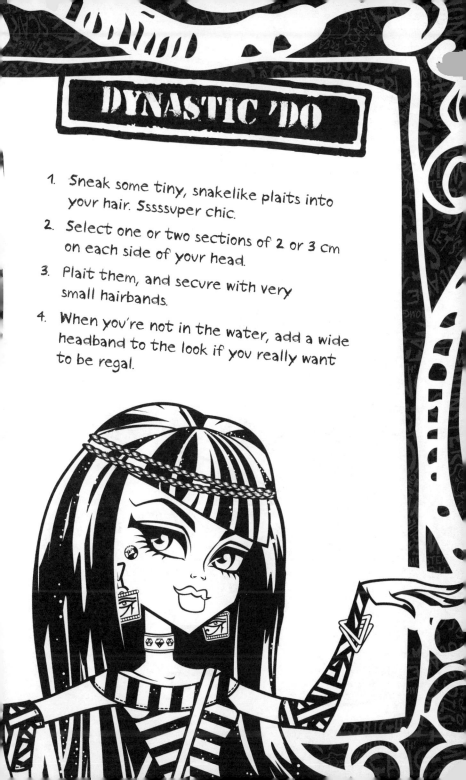

BEACHY KEEN

SANDTASTIC NAILS are imperative.

You'll need a clear top coat, black nail-art pen and turquoise and gold nail polishes.

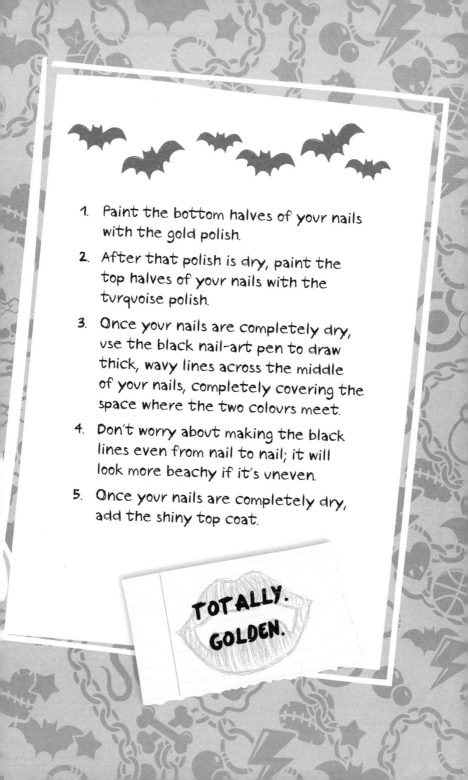

1. Paint the bottom halves of your nails with the gold polish.

2. After that polish is dry, paint the top halves of your nails with the turquoise polish.

3. Once your nails are completely dry, use the black nail-art pen to draw thick, wavy lines across the middle of your nails, completely covering the space where the two colours meet.

4. Don't worry about making the black lines even from nail to nail; it will look more beachy if it's uneven.

5. Once your nails are completely dry, add the shiny top coat.

TOTALLY.
GOLDEN.

GLOOM CASTLE

No **BEACH TRIP** is complete without a visit to a chic, vampire-friendly castle ... made out of sand. It's almost like being in Transylvania!

Architecture Guide

1. Live on the edge of danger — you have to make drip castles near the water's edge. Pick a spot not too near and not too far.

2. Dig a 'bowl' in the sand and let it fill with water, or fill a bucket with water and add some sand to it. The sand needs to be smooth, like wet mud.

3. Make a big mound of damp sand. You can add a fence around the mound if you'd like.

4. Take a handful of wet sand and rub your
   fingers together over the mound of sand.
   The wet sand will drip down, creating creepy
   gothic shapes.

5. Make the castle as large and intricate
   as you like.

6. Don't forget to put bats in the belfry!
   And maybe a nice heart in front of the door.

Frankie

INTERNATIONAL TRAVEL

You broaden your VISION when you travel internationally. You can visit my *bonita* home, Hexico, or there are so many other amazing places you can go. Scaris, Transylvania, Fangland — goregeous places all over the globe where you can see new things, experience new cultures and learn all about fashions you've never seen before. *Increíble!*

INTERNATIONAL PLANNING

What are three scare-ific sites you want to see around the world?

_____

_____

_____

_____

Where are three places you've been?

_____

_____

_____

Where are three places you want to go?

_____

_____

_____

If you are travelling internationally, you need to look your beast! You also need to bring some speciality items with you. And don't forget to keep an eye out for romance! Add your own items to the lists below.

Packing List:

- passport (so you can get through creep-stoms)
- plug adapters (to keep your iCoffin charged)
- translation book or app (to speak the fangvage)
- guidebook (to provide details on monster history)
- _____
- _____
- _____
- _____
- _____
- _____

Fashion List:

- chic scarf, perfume, smelly cheese (Scaris)
- bat wings, black cape, garlic (Transylvania)
- scary-cute bathing suit, sunscream, salsa (Hexico)
- _____
- _____
- _____
- _____
- _____
- _____

ROMAN HOWLIDAY

One of the beast parts of *international travel* is planning your ideal howliday. If you could go absolutely anyscare and do absolutely anything while you were there, what would you do? Write all about it here!

_____

_____

_____

_____

_____

Clawdeen

_____

_____

_____

_____

_____

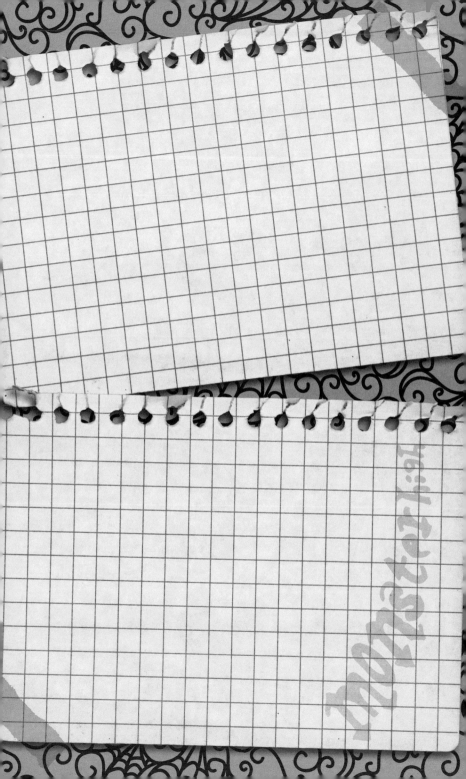

GARGOYLES ON A PLANE

Travelling **internationally** can be complex. Tick off the items on this list and be prepared.

- Make sure your water bottle is empty before you go through security. You can fill it up once you're through the gate.

- Be ready to take off your shoes and jewellery before going through the metal detector. Hope your claws are polished!

- Have your passport ready when you get to customs.

- Keep your luggage with you at all times.

IN-FRIGHT ENTERTAINMENT

- 💀 Listen closely to all safety instructions at the beginning of and during your flight.

- 💀 Pack the latest must-read novel on your list. You may be able to finish it!

- 💀 Bring a book of logic puzzles, corpsewords or boo-doku.

- 💀 Bring a notebook for writing spooky stories or sketching monsterpieces.

- 💀 Look through the in-fright magazine. Rank the items for sale on a silliness scale of 1 (for least silly) to 5 (for most silly).

- 💀 Don't fight with your siblings! Remember that other passengers are on the plane with you.

- 💀 Pack some yummy, healthy snacks. Also pack gum to chew during take-off and landing to keep your ears from popping.

- 💀 Study a beginner's guide to the language of the country you're visiting. Nothing is more Scarisian than understanding *un petit peu de français*.

SPEAKING THE FANGUAGE

Before you head overseas, you need to learn some KEY PHRASES in the fanguage of the country you're visiting. Using a language book or the internet, find the translations for these phrases and write them in so you have easy access to them.

Hello!

_____

_____

HOW ARE YOU?

_____

_____

WHAT IS YOUR NAME?

_____

_____

My name is _____

_____

_____

_____

It's nice to meet you.

_____

_____

_____

How much does that cost?

_____

_____

_____

WHERE ARE THE TOILETS?

_____

_____

_____

I'm looking for my family.

_____

_____

_____

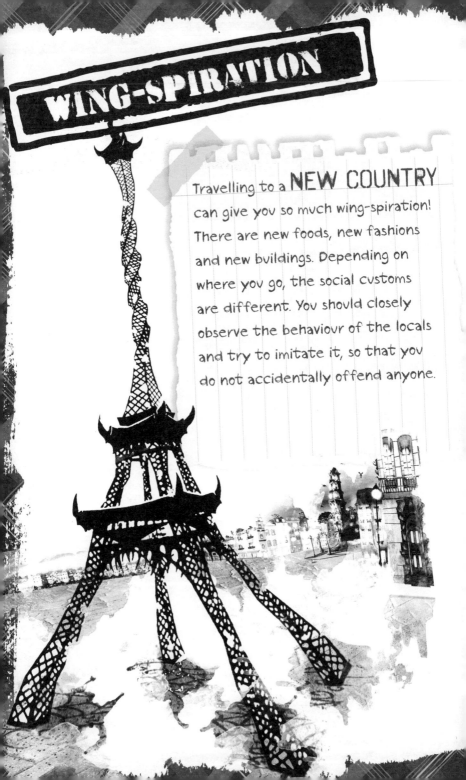

WING-SPIRATION

Travelling to a **NEW COUNTRY** can give you so much wing-spiration! There are new foods, new fashions and new buildings. Depending on where you go, the social customs are different. You should closely observe the behaviour of the locals and try to imitate it, so that you do not accidentally offend anyone.

LOCAL CLAWTURE

Some **CLAWSOME** places to visit in a new place are bootiful museums, the locations of important historical events and local markets. Write down some places that you will visit:

_____

_____

_____

_____

_____

_____

_____

_____

_____

_____

_____

_____

_____

_____

_____

INTERNATIONAL FASHION

One of the **BEAST** things you can do when enjoying another country is buy a fashion magazine to see what the local ghouls are wearing! Their clothes and accessories may not be available where you live, but you can use the magazines to come up with new and exciting fashion ideas. Go through the magazine and cut out the most fur-rocious pieces. Stick them here to inspire you!

PRETTY *in* PINK BUT BETTER *in* BLACK

SCALE MAIL

If you visit other country, least you can do for ghoulfriends is send them postcard. Make postcard extra special by personalizing. Bring stickers and marker pens with you. Buy postcard of bootiful local scenery and add own touches. You will need to buy local airmail stamp. Then drop in mail!

Draw your own postcard design for the country you are visiting:

Howlidays are full of fun, but sometimes it seems like there is *nothing* to do. It's horror-ble! But don't let boredom give you the boos. Nothing is sparkier than trying out things you've never done before, so when you are at your bats' end, try some of the activities on the next pages – they'll turn monster bleak into monster chic!

GHOUL-ENTEERING

Score some **KARMIC** savings by ghoul-enteering for your family and neighbours! Earn flowers to become a higher-level ghoul-enteer.

Each time you do anything on the ghoul-enteer list, you earn flowers!

- Carrying in the shopping = 1 FLOWER
- Washing a car = 1 FLOWER
- Taking out the rubbish = 1 FLOWER
- Keeping plants' skin shiny and green by helping out with a lawn or garden = 2 FLOWERS
- Walking a pet (such as a dog, bat or dragon) = 2 FLOWERS

Try to reach Ghoul-enempress before the howlidays end!

12 flowers: Junior Ghoul-enteer
16 flowers: Ghoul-enteer
20 flowers: Senior Ghoul-enteer
24 flowers: Ghoul-enprincess
28 flowers: Ghoul-enqueen
32 flowers: Ghoul-enempress

Track your **FLOWERS** with this chart!

SHOPPING	Car	Rubbish	PLANTS	PET

STREET MAUL

G*H*O*U*L, you need to raise some cash!
Try starting a business in your neighbourhood.
There are all kinds of clawsome companies
you could start.

- 💀 organize a scarage sale
- 💀 hold a car wash
- 💀 raise money for scarity
- 💀 sell spooky snacks

_____
_____
_____
_____
_____
_____
_____
_____

What are some of your own **BUSINESS** ideas?

Get to know the **ARCHITECTURE** in your neighbourhood, garden or even house or flat really, really well by drawing a monster map. Take careful notes on where all the streets, houses, bushes, hiding places and rooms are. Include all the detail that you can. For extra ghoulishness, add gravestones in the most creative places possible – and don't forget to add in some gargoyles, *bien sûr!* Gargoyles give buildings special protection from evil spirits.

SLINGING CABLES

DON'T FORGET
to keep in shape for fearleading!
Grab a skipping rope and
try these moves.

KEEP IT!
TOgETHER!
FRANKIE

Maybe you know this one already?

Basic Cable

1. Hold one end of the skipping rope in each hand, with the rope hanging behind you.

2. Swing the skipping rope forwards over your head and jump over it.

3. Keep going! See how many jumps you can do in a row.

4. Now add a cheer to the rhythm of your jumping:

M-O-N-S-T-E-R-S.

MONSTERS, MONSTERS,
YES, WE ARE!

CROSSED CABLE

1. Hold one end of the skipping rope in each hand, with the rope hanging behind you.

2. As you swing the rope forwards over your head to jump over it, cross your arms in front of you.

3. After you jump, bring your arms back to their original position.

4. Once you get the hang of it, you can count your jumps and add the cheer.

how bout you?

One-Legged Crossed Cable

Sometimes you cheer so hard that you lose a leg over it! Don't let that stop you, though. This jump is the same as Crossed Cables, but on one foot! Bend your other leg at the knee slightly so that it isn't touching the ground. Again, once you've mastered this, you can count your jumps and add in the cheer.

STUDY ANCIENT HISTORY

Get activity ideas from the **GHOSTS OF HOWLIDAYS PAST!** Ancient times were pretty spooky, so talk to three different adults about their favourite howliday activities from when they were young monsters. Write them here and then try them!

Spectra

Ghost of Howlidays Past - **No. 1**

Ghost name:

_____

_____

_____

How do you know this ghost?

_____

_____

_____

_____

_____

_____

What ideas did this ghost give you?

_____

_____

_____

_____

_____

_____

Ghost of Howlidays Past - **No. 2**

Ghost name:

_____

_____

_____

_____

_____

How do you know this ghost?

_____

_____

_____

_____

What ideas did this ghost give you?

_____

_____

_____

_____

Ghost of Howlidays Past - **No. 3**

Ghost name:

_____

_____

_____

_____

_____

How do you know this ghost?

_____

_____

_____

_____

_____

What ideas did this ghost give you?

_____

_____

_____

_____

_____

_____

INDOOR FREAK-TIVITIES

What's a ghoul supposed to do when it's RAINING bats and frogs? Take the party inside, that's what! But don't just watch television, play video games and text your ghoulfriends on your iCoffin. Instead, get moving! Otherwise, you might contract a case of the rainy-day boos.

List some fun indoor activities you like to do:

_____

_____

_____

_____

_____

_____

_____

ROCK THE CAPER

STRUTTING your stuff under the fright lights and singing your heart out while your fans howl your name? Well, now, what ghoul wouldn't want to be a rock star? And the first thing a rock star has to do is pick a band name.

Circle one of these howlarious names or come up with your own!

THE FAB FUR

Simone & Gargoyle

LED ZOMBELIN

THE VAMPETTES

Howl City

Write your name here: _____

Band name picked? Rockin'!
Now pick some scarylicious song titles!

Circle one of these spooktacular titles or write your own!

MATERIAL GHOUL

It Had to Be Boo

Starfright

I Fought the Claw

FANGNAM STYLE

Write your titles here:

" _____ "

" _____ "

" _____ "

And now it's time for the lyrics....

Here are some quick tips. Each verse is different and each line of the verse is different. Try making the first two lines rhyme with each other and the second two lines rhyme with each other. The chorus is the same every time. Try making the first, second and fourth lines the same and the third line different.

HERE'S AN EXAMPLE TO GET YOU STARTED:

Verse:

It's time to sing a monster song.
You know the words, so sing along.
Wave your hands up in the air,
Dancing like you just don't care.

CHORUS:

It's a monster party.
It's a monster party.
It's time to get wild.
It's a monster party.

Now write some lyrics of your own!

Verse:

_____

_____

_____

_____

CHORUS:

_____

_____

_____

_____

Verse:

_____

_____

_____

_____

CHORUS:

_____

_____

_____

_____

_____

Practise your song with whatever melody you want. You can use one you know (like the melody to _Twinkle, Twinkle, Little Star_) or you can make up your own as you go.

Now put on your most fangtastic outfit and perform your clawsome new tune for your family, your pets ... or your stuffed zombie toys!

HOWLSEKEEPING

In a big family, it's a ghoul's **RESPONSIBILITY** to help keep the crypt in good shape. And you can always turn your work into a dance party with wild music and a lot of energy! The more bows you earn, the more iCoffins you get to decorate over the page!

Each time you do anything on the crypt-keeping list, you earn bows!

- 💀 Dusting = 1 bow
- 💀 Emptying the dishwasher = 1 bow
- 💀 Watering plants = 1 bow
- 💀 Feeding pets (like cats, snakes or owls) = 1 bow
- 💀 Folding and putting away the clothes washing = 2 bows
- 💀 Tidying your room = 4 bows

Track your **bows** with this chart!

DUSTING	Dishes	plants	PETS	clothes	ROOM

Turn the page and decorate the number of iCoffins you've earned, according to the chart below.

12 bows: 1 iCoffin	24 bows: 4 iCoffins
16 bows: 2 iCoffins	28 bows: 5 iCoffins
20 bows: 3 iCoffins	32 bows: 6 iCoffins

FEARLEADING DANCE

A fearleading dance has to wow. It has to amaze. It has to make the audience say, "Oh my rah!" Are you up to the challenge of choreographing your own ghoulish dance routine for the Dance of the Delightfully Dead? Good. Let's go, ghouls!

Choreography Guide

1. Choreograph your dance in pieces, eight counts at a time (the counts are the beats of the music).

2. Pick a golden song with a good beat.

3. Start out with an eye-catching Egyptian pose.

4. Get the crowd's attention by not doing anything for the first eight counts.

5. At the beginning of your dance, use simpler moves, like 'step together, step touch'. Get more complicated as you go and bring out the big leaps and turns in the finale.

6. Strike a big pose right before the music ends. Stay in position and listen to all that applause!

7. Take a big bow. You've earned it!

Don't forget to put together the perfect costume before you perform. Something fun. Something sparkly. Something with tights underneath!

SCARY STORIES WITH GHOULIA

A story could have many different endings. This story has a beginning, but the end is up to you. Write about the ghoul and her favourite things. Include a few of her friends and family members. Then show what terrorific event happened to her over the howlidays and how she handled it.

Once upon a time, there was a ghoul with

deadly charm. She was on howliday and she ...

_____

_____

_____

_____

_____

_____

_____

_____

_____

_____

Ghoulia

Just because this story is finished doesn't mean you have to stop! You could write a story with different characters but the same first line. Or you could even write a different story about the same characters!

FRANKENVENTIONS WITH FRANKIE

Some of the **SPARKIEST** new stuff is made from recycled parts! You can get freaky chic clothes at a charity shop and update them with your own touch. You can use an empty bottle to grow a houseplant. You can even stitch your old T-shirts into a creeperific quilted blanket.

What other things could you make out of recycled parts? Write down your wildest ideas – like turning kites and tights into working bat wings! What other Frankenventions could you make?

Now list some **IDEAS** you can actually try – without having access to a scientific laboratory, that is.

_____

_____

_____

_____

_____

_____

_____

_____

_____

_____

_____

_____

_____

_____

_____

_____

Try making some of your Frankenventions come to life!

YOUR GHOULFRIENDS ARE WITH YOU IN SPIRIT

Even if you don't **see** your ghoulfriends every day, they're the beast friends you have. Would one of your friends make a good ghost or zombie? Do you have a friend who would look clawsome with fangs, wings and violet skin? Let your creative fires burn and draw them all here!

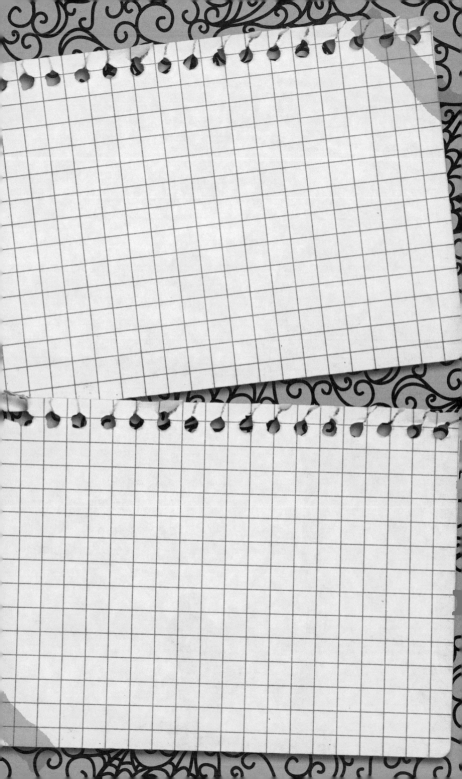

PETRIFIED

Venus

Pets **FEAR** you up when you're feeling down and help you stay envined with nature. So why not make a new pet for yourself and for each of your friends?

You'll need:

- card
- scissors
- glue
- pencil
- felt-tip pens
- 30 cm of thin ribbon
- glitter (optional)
- sequins (optional)

Instructions:

1. Using pencil on card, draw an animal no larger than a quarter of a page. Start with a simple shape, like a cat or frog, and then add fangs, horns, wings or other monster parts.

2. Cut out the animal.

3. Decorate it with markers. You can add glitter and sequins too. Now think of a name for your new pet!

4. Cut out a rectangular piece of card that is a bit more than double the size of your pet. Carefully fold the paper in half, like a birthday card. Your pet will go inside the card.

5. Using felt-tip pens (and glitter and sequins if you like) decorate the front of the card with your pet's name.

Continued on the next page!

6. Glue the ribbon horizontally across the back of the card and set it aside.

7. Cut a lengthwise strip of card. Make it a little bit thinner than your animal.

8. Make a fan: from the end, fold 2 cm of the paper forwards to touch the strip. Holding this together, fold 2 cm backwards, and so on until the end.

9. Glue one end of the fan to your pet and set a heavy book on it to help it stay in place while it dries.

10. After it's dry, glue the other end of the fan to the inside of the card (where a message would usually be printed). With the card open flat, place the fan in pre-springing position. Again, set the book on your pet to help it stay in place while it dries.

11. Once this is dry, close the card and tie the ribbon around it in a bow.

When you untie the ribbon and open the card, your pet will spring out at you!

THE END IS NEAR

Watch your clocks, **GHOULS!**
The howlidays are winding down and there are a few things you should strap into your schedule before it's over. You won't be able to face yourself if you don't get your cogs' worth out of summer – you can count on that!

Robecca

Visit a SCREAM PARK!

If you haven't been to one yet this summer (well, even if you have), take this chance to ride some scary-fast ghoulercoasters and squeal louder than the wheels of a freight train.

SCREAM PARK TIPS:

- For shorter queues and steam-free skin, go on a cloudy day (but not a rainy one)!
- Don't forget your fashion! Maybe wear some closed-toe shoes, a cute denim skirt and a lightweight top. Plus some oversized jewellery, of course!
- If the park will let you leave for lunch, pack a scarylicious picnic in a cool box.
- When the queue for your favourite ride is short, go again and again!
- Always, always, always strap yourself in.

SNACK ATTACK

Summer is best time for **ice scream**.
It is also being the best time for brain freeze.
And scareberries. This makes me hungry.
Try this recipe!

Scareberry Shortcake

You'll need:

- 1 scoop of vanilla ice scream (per serving)
- 1 plain sponge cake
- 1 small pot of whipping cream
- 1 punnet of blueberries
- 1 punnet of strawberries

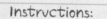

Instructions:

1. Rinse the blueberries and strawberries.
2. With an adult's help, hull and chop the strawberries. Set aside.
3. With an adult's help, cut the plain sponge cake into individual servings.
4. Put one scoop of ice scream on each plain sponge cake serving.

5. In a large bowl, whip the whipping cream with an electric whisk until stiff peaks form (ask an adult to help you!). Then add some cream to each serving.
6. Sprinkle a handful of blueberries and a handful of strawberries on top of each serving.

YUM!!!

HAZY DAISY CHAINS

Make a **SPIRITED** fashion statement with flowery jewellery fit for a summer monster. You can make daisy chains for yourself and for all your cousins and friends. You can wear them as necklaces, bracelets and even crowns. Qué linda!

Making Hazy Daisy Chains

1. Find a patch of daisies and make sure you're allowed to pick them. (You could also buy daisies or use another flower, like clovers.)

2. Pick several daisies.

3. Take one daisy and, using your thumbnail, put a 1 cm slit near the bottom of the stem.

4. Now take a second daisy and slide its stem through the slit. Now they're linked!

5. Keep repeating the previous two steps until you've reached your desired length.

6. To finish the chain, make a 2 cm slit in your final daisy, instead of a 1 cm slit. Put the head of your first daisy through this slit. (Remove the petals if necessary.)

7. Wear your daisy chain with pride!

GO FIN DEEP

You're stoked to see your *mates* every day when school starts, but you'll miss getting your flippers wet once the weather cools down. So take one last dip in a freshwater monster's foyer while you still can!

Swimming Tips

- Now's the time to show off how many laps you can do. Break out any cool tricks you've learned while you're at it!

- Bring a beach ball to the pool for some water volleyball, water polo or that old classic, catch.

- Remember to wear sunscream and drink plenty of water. But not pool water! (Not even freshies like to drink chlorine.)

SHOP UNTIL YOU DROP

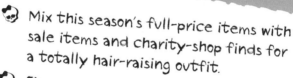

For totally clawsome back-to-school fashion, make one last trip to your favourite shop! Try these fashion tips!

- Mix this season's full-price items with sale items and charity-shop finds for a totally hair-raising outfit.

- Shop around! Browse several shops before picking out what you just *HAVE* to have.

- Accessories can change a whole outfit! Cardigans, jean jackets, scarves, hairbands and chunky jewellery are perfect for autumn.

BATTY BACK-TO-SCHOOL FUN

THE HOWLIDAYS IN REVIEW....

What fiery trips and fangtastic fun did you get into?

Whether you travelled abroad, went to Gloom Beach, had a vamping adventure or went to camp, you did new things and met new people. One of the best parts of the howlidays is remembering how much fun they were. If you write it down now, it can inspire you later.

Did you go on a **trip away**? What did you do there?

_____

_____

_____

_____

_____

_____

_____

_____

Did you meet new *ghoulfriends*? What do you like about them?

_____

_____

_____

_____

_____

_____

_____

_____

_____

_____

What was the most *clawsome* outfit you wore?

What was the **MOST TERRORIFIC** thing you did?

What was the **LEAST TERRORIFIC** thing you did?

What did you **NOT** do that you want to do **NEXT** howlidays?

THE FIRST DAY BACK

Making a first IMPRESSION is always important.
Just ask the Sphinx. *Nobody* forgets about her, do they?
To make sure you're a big hit, design some ghoul-amorous
ways to vamp up your look on your first day back at school.
You'll need to abide by your school's uniform rules,
but you can still look freaky chic!

Back to school means back to snacks!
It is important for a growing vampire
to eat a variety of healthy nibbles.
Here's a list of yummy monster snacks
to put in your lunchbox!

☐ banana

☐ carrot sticks

☐ apple

☐ yoghurt pot

☐ grapes

☐ mixed nuts

☐ _____

☐ _____

☐ _____

☐ _____

☐ _____

☐ _____

☐ _____

☐ _____

☐ _____

☐ _____

☐ _____

☐ _____

☐ _____

☐ _____

DEADULE

Keeping up with your **SCHEDULE** in the new school year is as important as keeping your claws clean. You'll need some school supplies to make sure you can keep track of your classes and schoolwork!

- 💀 daily planner
- 💀 pencil case
- 💀 pencils and pens
- 💀 rubbers
- 💀 ringbinders
- 💀 paper

- 💀 _____
- 💀 _____
- 💀 _____
- 💀 _____
- 💀 _____
- 💀 _____
- 💀 _____
- 💀 _____
- 💀 _____
- 💀 _____
- 💀 _____
- 💀 _____
- 💀 _____
- 💀 _____

Toralei

PASS THE MONSTER

The **howlidays** may be over, but the fun never stops. Get in the mood for Deadvcation by playing a back-to-school game with your ghoulfriends!

Instructions:

1. All ghouls stand in a circle.

2. Ghoul A turns to the ghoul on her right (Ghoul B) and makes a monster noise with a monster face.

3. Ghoul B passes the noise and face to Ghoul C, who passes it to Ghoul D and so on.

4. Keep passing the monster from one ghoul to another, round and round the circle.

5. Even though you'll try to match the noise and face exactly, it will gradually change into a new monster noise and face.

6. Add in hoof and claw movements — shake your fur! Howl! Go wild!

FITTING IN IS SO OUT!

SO SPOOKTACULAR!

THE HOWLIDAYS HAVE COME TO AN END!

You've had a pretty **scary** howliday, jam-packed with trips, all the family time a ghoul could need and plenty o f *ghoul-amour.*

Maybe you WROTE a song or story, solved a PUZZLE or **choreographed** a dance. Just because the howlidays are over doesn't mean the fun has to **STOP!** You can think of sor BUSINESS ideas or Frankenventions for the rest of the year a you can write notes to your friends in UNCREEPABLE cod

So keep the **fangtastic** times going. Have a scary school year. And stay goregeous, *ghoulfriend!*

Answer to Zombie-rific Wordsearch.

A	D	O	C	I	X	E	H	J	Z	G	R	P	Z	U
G	M	M	T	L	O	H	Y	C	S	C	A	R	I	S
G	X	L	L	A	B	T	E	K	S	A	C	M	T	P
J	B	Z	G	N	I	D	A	E	L	R	A	E	F	C
M	K	G	D	I	K	W	N	S	X	N	W	N	N
M	Y	A	W	R	T	O	E	U	J	L	H	I	O	J
O	V	Q	A	G	S	D	O	Y	J	Z	F	I	E	J
N	B	C	L	K	L	E	M	X	L	F	H	E	G	U
S	Y	K	C	O	G	D	D	A	O	S	M	I	A	N
T	O	A	G	E	E	E	T	C	A	O	X	Z	T	G
E	J	U	R	U	U	I	I	L	S	G	F	N	L	G
R	O	O	D	C	P	J	F	W	E	P	I	H	O	D
S	G	T	E	A	J	A	A	E	O	R	H	L	V	S
T	D	G	C	G	J	L	C	T	M	P	V	Y	Y	C
R	I	A	R	E	C	X	N	I	H	P	S	F	V	T

If you had a clawsome
time with this

Howliday
Journal

don't miss the

Party Journal!

Available from all
good book shops.

Goodbye from MONSTER HIGH!